Noel!

Songs for the Christmas season

Illustrated by

ANNABEL SPENCELEY

ff

Faber & Faber
in association with
Faber Music

Contents

Ding dong! Merrily on high	1	The holly and the ivy	17
Past three o'clock	2	Mary's boy child	18
God rest you merry, gentlemen	4	Rocking	20
Rudolph the red-nosed reindeer	6	While shepherds watched	21
Deck the hall	9	Wassail	22
I saw three ships	10	The twelve days of Christmas	24
Little donkey	11	Good King Wenceslas	26
We three kings of Orient are	12	We wish you a merry Christmas	28
Silent night	14	Jingle bells	30

© 1990 by Faber Music Ltd
First published in 1990 by Faber & Faber Ltd
in association with Faber Music Ltd
3 Queen Square London WC1N 3AU
Music arrangements by Susan Belsham © 1990 by Faber Music Ltd
Illustrations © 1990 by Annabel Spenceley
Music drawn by Christopher Hinkins
Typesetting by Goodfellow & Egan, Cambridge
Printed in England.

Past three o'clock

2. Seraph choir singeth,
   Angel bell ringeth:
   Hark how they rhyme it,
   Time it, and chime it.
   Past three o'clock, etc.

3. Mid earth rejoices
   Hearing such voices
   Ne'er-to-fore so well
   Carolling Nowell.
   Past three o'clock, etc.

God rest you merry, gentlemen

God rest you merry, gentlemen

Rudolph the red-nosed reindeer

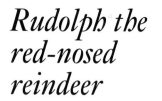

Ru-dolph the red - nosed rein-deer had a ve-ry shi-ny nose,

And if you e - ver saw it you would e -ven say it glows!

All of the o - ther rein - deer used to laugh and call him names,
Then all the rein - deer loved him, and they shout-ed out with glee:

They ne - ver let poor Ru - dolph join in a - ny rein - deer games.
'Ru - dolph the red - nosed rein - deer you'll go down in his - to - ry!'

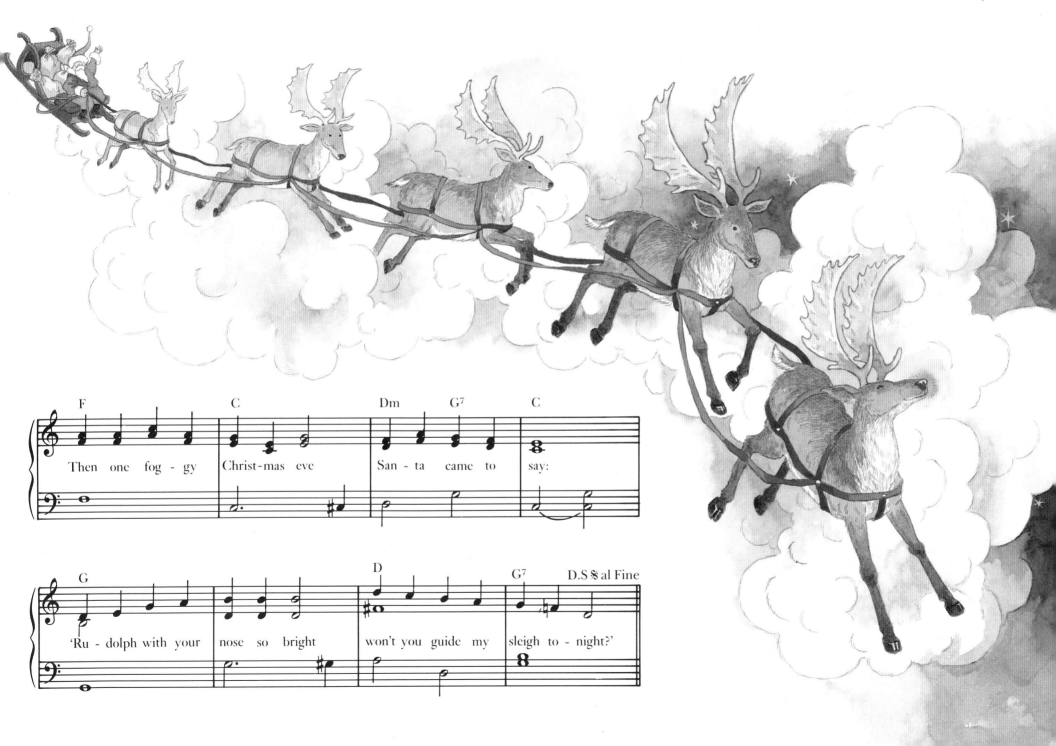

Deck the hall

2. See the flowing bowl before us,
   Fa la la la la, la la la la.
   Strike the harp and join the chorus,
   Fa la *etc.*
   Follow me in merry measure,
   Fa la *etc.*
   While I sing of beauty's treasure,
   Fa la *etc.*

3. Fast away the old year passes,
   Fa la *etc.*
   Hail the new, ye lads and lasses,
   Fa la *etc.*
   Laughing, quaffing all together,
   Fa la *etc.*
   Heedless of the wind and weather,
   Fa la *etc.*

I saw
three ships

1. I saw three ships come sail-ing in, On Christ-mas day, on Christ-mas day, I
2. And what was in those ships all three? On Christ-mas day, on Christ-mas day, And

saw three ships come sail-ing in, On Christ-mas day in the morn-ing.
what was in those ships all three? On Christ-mas day in the morn-ing.

3. Our saviour Christ and his lady,
4. Pray, whither sailed those ships all three?
5. O, they sailed into Bethlehem.
6. And all the bells on earth shall ring.
7. Then let us all rejoice amain!

Little donkey

We three kings of Orient are

O _____ star of won - der, star of

night, star with ro - yal beau - ty

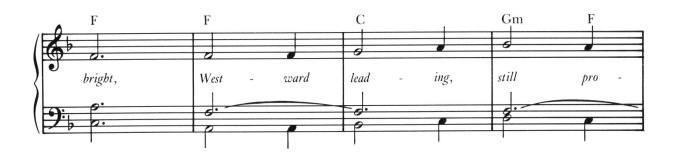

bright, West - ward lead - ing, still pro -

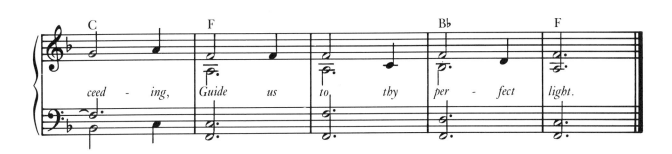

ceed - ing, Guide us to thy per - fect light.

2. Born a King on Bethlehem plain,
   Gold I bring to crown him again,
   King for ever, ceasing never,
   Over us all to reign.
   O star of wonder, etc.

3. Frankincense to offer have I,
   Incense owns a deity nigh.
   Prayer and praising, All men raising
   Worship Him, God most high.
   O star of wonder, etc.

4. Myrrh is mine; its bitter perfume
   Breathes a life of gathering gloom,
   Sorrowing, sighing, bleeding, dying,
   Sealed in a stone-cold tomb.
   O star of wonder, etc.

Silent night

Si - lent night, ho - ly night, All is calm,

all is bright, Round yon vir - gin mo - ther and child, Ho - ly

The holly and the ivy

3. The holly bears a prickle,
   As sharp as any thorn,
   And Mary bore sweet Jesus Christ
   On Christmas day in the morn.
       O the rising, etc.

4. The holly and the ivy
   When they are both full grown,
   Of all the trees that are in the wood,
   The holly bears the crown.
       O the rising, etc.

Mary's boy child

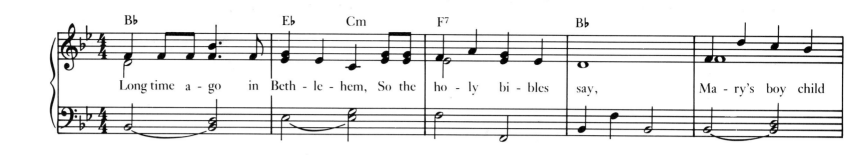

Long time a - go in Beth - le - hem, So the ho - ly bi - bles say, Ma - ry's boy child

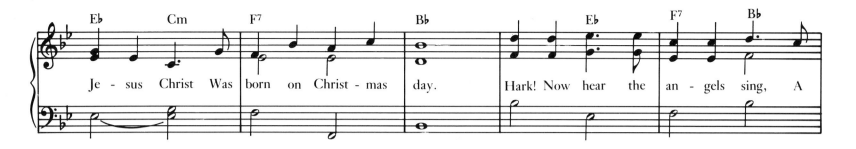

Je - sus Christ Was born on Christ - mas day. Hark! Now hear the an - gels sing, A

new King born to - day. And man will live for e - ver - more Be - cause of Christ - mas day.

Rocking

1. Lit - tle Je - sus sweet-ly sleep, do not stir, We will lend a coat of fur.
2. Ma - ry's lit - tle ba - by, sleep, sweet - ly sleep, Sleep in com - fort, slum - ber deep;

We will rock you, rock you, rock you, We will rock you, rock you, rock you:

See the fur to keep you warm, Snug - ly round your ti - ny form.
We will serve you all we can, Dar - ling, dar - ling lit - tle man.

Reproduced from the Oxford Book of Carols
by permission of Oxford University Press

1. While shep - herds watched their flocks by night, All seat - ed on the ground, The
2. 'Fear not', said he (for migh - ty dread Had seized their troub - led mind); The 'Glad

an - gel of the Lord came down And glo - ry shone a - round.
tid - ings of the great joy I bring To you and all man - kind.'

3. 'To you in David's town this day
   Is born of David's line
   A Saviour, who is Christ the Lord;
   And this shall be the sign:'

4. 'The heavenly Babe you there shall find
   To human view displayed,
   All meanly wrapped in swathing bands,
   And in a manger laid.'

5. All glory be to God on high,
   And to the earth be peace;
   Good-will henceforth from heaven to men
   Begin and never cease.

Wassail

1. Was- sail,___ was - sail,___ all o - ver the town!___ Our toast it is
2. So here is to Cher - ry and to his right cheek,___ Our Pray God send our

white, and our ale ___ it ___ is brown, Our ___ bowl ___ it ___ is ___ made of the
mas - ter a good ___ piece ___ of beef, And a good ___ piece ___ of ___ beef that ___

white ma - ple tree; With the was - sail - ing bowl We'll drink ___ to thee.
may we all see; With the was - sail - ing bowl We'll drink ___ to thee.

Reproduced from the Oxford Book of Carols
by permission of Oxford University Press

3. Then here's to the maid in the lily-white smock,
Who tripped to the door and slipped back the lock!
Who tripped to the door and pulled back the pin,
For to let these jolly wassailers in.

The twelve days of Christmas

The twelve days of Christmas

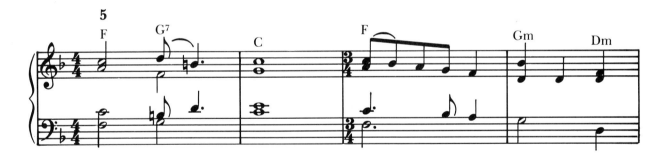

1. On the first day of Christmas
   My true love sent to me
   A partridge in a pear tree.

2. On the second day . . .
   Two turtle doves.

3. On the third day . . .
   Three french hens.

4. On the fourth day . . .
   Four coloured birds.

5. On the fifth day . . .
   Five gold rings.

6. On the sixth day . . .
   Six geese a-laying.

7. On the seventh day . . .
   Seven swans a-swimming.

8. On the eighth day . . .
   Eight maids a-milking.

9. On the ninth day . . .
   Nine drummers drumming.

10. On the tenth day . . .
    Ten pipers piping.

11. On the eleventh day . . .
    Eleven ladies dancing.

12. On the twelfth day . . .
    Twelve lords a-leaping.

'Five Gold Rings' extract by Frederic Austin
reproduced by permission of Novello & Company Ltd.

Good King Wenceslas

1. Good King Wen - ces - las looked out, On the feast of Ste - phen,
2. 'Hi - ther, page, and stand by me, If thou know'st it, tell - ing,

When the snow lay
Yon - der pea - sant,

round a - bout, Deep, and crisp, and e - ven: Bright - ly shone the moon that night,
who is he? Where and what his dwell - ing?' 'Sire, he lives a good league hence,

Though the frost was cru - el,
Un - der - neath the moun - tain,

When a poor man
Right a - gainst the

came in sight,
for - est fence,

Gath' - ring win - ter
By Saint Ag - nes'

fu
foun

el.
tain.'

3. 'Bring me flesh, and bring me wine,
Bring me pine logs hither;
Thou and I will see him dine,
When we bear them thither.'
Page and monarch, forth they went,
Forth they went together;
Through the rude wind's wild lament
And the bitter weather.

4. 'Sire, the night is darker now,
And the wind blows stronger;
Fails my heart, I know not how;
I can go no longer.'
'Mark my footsteps good, my page;
Tread thou in them boldly;
Thou shalt find the winter's rage
Freeze thy blood less coldly.'

5. In his master's steps he trod,
Where the snow lay dinted;
Heat was in the very sod
Which the saint had printed.
Therefore, Christian men, be sure,
Wealth or rank possessing,
Ye who now will bless the poor,
Shall yourselves find blessing.

We wish you a merry Christmas

3. For we all like figgy pudding,
   We all like figgy pudding,
   For we all like figgy pudding,
   So bring some out here.
      Good tidings, etc.

4. And we won't go until we've got some,
   We won't go until we've got some,
   And we won't go until we've got some,
   So bring some out here.
      Good tidings, etc.